W9-BTN-002

Meet Clara

Clara's Cake

lara is coming
ome from school.

I have mail
for you.

Baking
contest!

I love
contests!

Clara signs up for the contest.

The contest is in two days!

Clara's sisters want to enter, too.

Sign us up, too, please. O[ur] nails are wet[.]

Ow!

Ruff!

Clara Saves the Day

Clara is on her way to school.

I hope I am not late.

Oh, dear.

Oops!

Clara is late to school—again.

Do not be late for the class trip tomorrow.

Sorry, Miss Priss. I got tangled up.